Thomson and Thompson

by Michael Farr

EGMONT

EGMONT

We bring stories to life

Art copyright © Hergé/Moulinsart 2007
Text copyright © Michael Farr/Moulinsart 2007

First published in Great Britain in 2007
by Egmont UK Limited
239 Kensington High Street, London W8 6SA

Originally designed and published by Éditions Moulinsart

ISBN 978 1 4052 3061 2

1 3 5 7 9 10 8 6 4 2

Printed and bound in Belgium

Among the cast of *The Adventures of Tintin* a memorable role is played by the Thom(p)sons who provide an invaluable and predictable dose of slapstick humour as the accident-prone detectives sure to follow the false trail and, in the best tradition of French farce, as the policemen who are invariably late. "Good morning... Er... Here we are at last..." the battered and bruised detectives declare on the penultimate page of *The Blue Lotus* as they catch up with Tintin. "To be precise: good morning. Here we are, last as usual..." By the time they arrive, it is Tintin who is in control of the situation and on top of the detective work. He behaves, as Snowy remarks, like Sherlock Holmes, while they play the part of the rigidly opinionated police inspectors created by authors such as Sir Arthur Conan Doyle or Agatha Christie – whose stories were familiar to Hergé – that draw the wrong conclusions and at the denouement are loathe to admit their mistakes. However similar in appearance and name Hergé's blundering detectives may be to each other they are not, unlike his father and uncle on whom to some extent they were modelled, twins. He liked to tell an anecdote of how a scrap merchant in Brussels years later collected some bundles of old *Tintin* magazines from a colleague and told him how he lived opposite the real Dupondt (the original French names for the Thom(p)sons). On checking the address, Hergé found that the man did indeed live across the street from his father and uncle!

Michael Farr

Incompetent, clumsy buffoons despite their best intentions; they rank as kings of comedy slapstick

Thomson and Thompson

The first appearance of the Thom(p)sons; frame from *Cigars of the Pharaoh*.

Tʜᴏᴍsᴏɴ ᴀɴᴅ Tʜᴏᴍᴘsᴏɴ – or the Thom(p)sons for ease of reference – are veteran, enduring figures in *The Adventures of Tintin* appearing to a lesser or greater extent in 20 out of the altogether 24 books. Excluding of course Tintin and Snowy, no other characters can boast so many appearances, not even Captain Haddock who, arriving later, was to star in 16 adventures.

It would be a distinguished record if only they were not such professional failures as detectives. However, they rate highly as accident-prone buffoons during the age of Charlie Chaplin and Laurel and Hardy. Chronically clumsy, they are constantly slipping up or tripping over, both physically and verbally. They are, in modern terms largely unrecognised at the time, both dyspraxic and dyslexic.

They are, moreover, exceedingly naive, hopelessly narrow-minded, and obnoxiously full of self-importance. The two are, in short, pompous, credulous fools with a penchant for fancy dress. Though hardly endearing, they bring hilarity to the adventures. The bumbling detectives provide the necessary counterpoint to the rough and tumble, the excitement of the narrative, allowing a necessary relaxation of tension.

Their conceit is insufferable. Having with Tintin and Snowy tackled Omar Ben Salaad in *The Crab with the Golden Claws*, Thomson calls headquarters and takes credit with Thompson for unmasking a gang of opium smugglers.

Right: Frame from *The Crab with the Golden Claws*.

My old friends
omson and Thompson.

FRIENDS DESPITE EVERYTHING

Despite more often than not seeking to arrest Tintin in the earlier adventures, or at least impeding inquiries with their incompetence, an at times uneasy friendship develops between the ace reporter/investigator and the bungling police pair. In *The Blue Lotus*, their superior Dawson, the corrupt Chief of Police of the International Settlement, sends them with travel permits and a Chinese safe-conduct to arrest Tintin. "A rotten job!" Thomson tells Thompson as they leave. "Just our luck!... Ordered to arrest a friend!"

OCCASIONALLY INSPIRED, RARELY COURAGEOUS

The two detectives have their inspired moments, even if dictated by duty. In *Cigars of the Pharaoh*, their first adventure, in the unlikely guise of Arab ladies, they organise Tintin's survival of execution by firing squad... in order to arrest him "as a drug smuggler and gun-runner!" Arriving in India, they show surprising inventiveness in saving the life of Snowy – about to be sacrificed on the altar of Siva – so as to use him to track down his master. "How wrong I was. They're

really pretty good chaps!" Snowy declares appreciatively.

Their character is often questionable, combining stupidity, arrogance and cowardice, but finally in *Tintin and the Picaros* they redeem themselves heroically, refusing first to be cowed by the vitriol of the military tribunal, and then showing unusual steadfastness and sangfroid – admittedly bolstered by alcohol – before the firing squad.

Despite being detectives and enforcers of the law, they are generally far from courageous. They have a particular fear of the supernatural. In the rooms and corridors of the rocket research centre in Syldavia in *Destination Moon*, they take fright after mistaking each other's skeletal x-ray image for a ghost, and end up "arresting" an anatomical skeleton in the osteology department. "You needn't pretend to be dead my friend; you've had it this time," Thompson declares as they march the skeleton away. Their next funk comes as they jump onto a chair terrified after encountering white mice that have escaped from Captain Haddock's space suit. Courage does not course in their veins.

THE ACTUAL MODELS

As often with Hergé he drew on more than one source for his inspira-
tion. The most immediate came from home. His father, Alexis Remi,
had an identical twin brother, Léon. They both sported moustaches,
dressed in the same fashion and shared at least one catchphrase
with the detectives – the French "je dirais même plus!" (freely trans-
lated in the English editions as "To be precise!") that is used in one

Facing page: The inseparable twins Alexis and Léon Remi, in 1928.

Right: The entry hall of the Studios Hergé, where two walking canes and a pair of bowler hats await their owners...

form or other more than 60 times during the course of the adventures.

On Sunday mornings the Remi twins would don their bowler hats, pick up either their walking canes or, depending on the weather, umbrellas and venture forth for their weekly constitutional. This ritual left an image firmly imprinted on the young Georges's mind. While later acknowledging this, Hergé maintained that he was not consciously thinking of them when he created the Thom(p)sons. Yet subconsciously the recollection was clearly there. To this day, as a tribute to the Remi brothers and the Thom(p)sons, a pair of bowler hats and two sticks hang expectantly on their pegs – adding a touch of surrealism reminiscent of fellow Belgian artist René Magritte – in the lobby of the Studios Hergé in the Avenue Louise in Brussels.

Heavens, what an escape! We're all in one piece... If that machine hadn't stopped suddenly we'd be coming out of here in neat little cans.

I wonder how often, they have that sort of accident!

Above: Modern mechanisation, frame from *Tintin in America*.

Left: Charlie Chaplin, a prototype for the Thom(p)sons.

Right: Charlie Chaplin, Director and star of *Modern Times* (1936).

Hergé embarked on *The Adventures of Tintin* during the heyday of that bowler-hatted, cane-flourishing, anti-hero Charlie Chaplin. Born in London in 1889, worldwide fame came with the silent cinema and his portrayal of a down-trodden tramp-like character with smudge moustache, bowler hat and cane in The Gold Rush (1925), *The Circus* (1928), *City Lights* (1931) and *Modern Times* (1936), showing man's predicament in the machine-age, a subject Hergé had already explored in *Tintin in America* (1932). Hergé was a great fan of Chaplin and keenly aware of contemporary cinema and some of its techniques which he tried to apply to the strip cartoon.

Speech bubble: *Aren't you ashamed, at your age? Quarrelling over such trifles! Now, that's all over, isn't it?*

Of course there were two other contemporary comedy film stars with bowler hats: Laurel and Hardy. Their childish contrition could be echoed by the Thom(p)sons.

There is too the remarkable cover of *Le Miroir* of March 1919 in Hergé's archive. It shows two bowler-hatted, moustached detectives with a suspect. Their resemblance to the Thom(p)sons is staggering.

D.R.

Thomson

Thompson

SPOT THE DIFFERENCES

One fundamental difference between the Thom(p)sons and Alexis and Léon Remi is the fact that the detectives are neither twins nor identical. They cannot be brothers either, for though similar their surnames are different – that 'p, as in psychology.'

Moreover, their moustaches are significantly not trimmed in quite the same manner. Thompson has it clipped straighter, while Thomson allows a slight, distinctive twirl at the ends.

There is the wonderful moment in the last completed adventure, *Tintin and the Picaros*, where the public prosecutor accuses the pair of cultivating their moustaches in order "to appear as loyal supporters of General Tapioca and the noble ideology of Kûrvi-Tasch." Thompson protests furiously: "That's a lie!... We've been wearing moustaches since we were born!" Thomson adding: "To be precise: we're worn bearing them!"

Thomson

Thompson

FIRST APPEARANCES

The Thom(p)sons real debut comes in *Cigars of the Pharaoh* (1934) where in the first black and white French version they are identified mysteriously but unmemorably as agents X33 and X33 bis (in English X33 and X33A), only later being named Dupond et Dupont in French and Thomson and Thompson in English. However, when Hergé revised *Tintin in the Congo* (1931) – the second of the adventures – for its 1946 colour edition, he defied the chronology of the Tintin books and inserted in its opening departure scene the Thom(p)sons on the railway platform in place of the two porters he had before. "It's apparently a young reporter who's leaving for Africa..." one says to the other. Their role in this early flawed adventure extends no further.

The Thom(p)sons' true introduction into the adventures in *Cigars of the Pharaoh* is full of menace. They are first seen peering through the deck doorway as Tintin enters his cabin on the M.S. Isis. They rap aggressively on the cabin door, enter and, striking identical poses, announce in chorus his

arrest. It is an unfortunate start to a relationship that for several adventures is dogged by uncertainty with the Thom(p)sons spending more time mistakenly pursuing Tintin rather than the actual malefactors.

THE COMEDY OF THE SITUATION

The comic effect of the Thom(p)sons and their escapades is tailored according to the plot of each adventure in which they make their mark. Their professional status as detectives allows them to slip into the narrative quite naturally. The misunderstandings, blunders, their spectacular and repeated tumbles and falls, the absurd fancy dressing, all offer relief at the right moment at the expense of the ridiculous pair of sleuths.

So in *Prisoners of the Sun*, having lost Tintin and Haddock in South America, the Thom(p)sons reappear later in half a dozen mostly single-frame cameos defying time and distance by popping up in greatly contrasting geographic locations in a pendulum-led search, "like Professor Calculus; that'll put us on their track." From Brussels and Paris, they travel to an unspecified but suitably deep coal mine, the Egyptian desert in front of Sphinx and pyramids, a funfair with dodgems and the shivering expanse of the Antarctic with its attendant penguins. While comic, it also has a surreal quality, notably the images of the suited, bowler-hatted figures under the blazing desert sun or amid the frozen Antarctic expanse, reminiscent of the painter Magritte.

They end up in the desert in *Land of Black Gold*, which by its conclusion has far-reaching capillary consequences for them. But

they begin in great good humour motoring along and singing to a melody inspired by the popular *chansonnier* Charles Trenet until – **BOOM!** – their car blows up and soon afterwards so does Thompson's lighter, fuelled by the same petrol they topped up with at the garage. They gain employment as mechanics with a vehicle recovery firm in an attempt to

get to the bottom of the blight of explosions affecting motorists, but are soon sacked for incompetence.

Once in Arabia, they set out in a bright red jeep, Thompson as usual at the wheel. They fall victim to a series of real or imagined mirages but continue on their way, memorably driving round and round in a circle following their own tracks, an idea which occurred to Hergé after he saw a photograph in *National Geographic Magazine* of vehicle tracks imprinted in the desert sand. Somehow they find Tintin in a sandstorm and subsequently, dropping off at the wheel, they crash sacrilegiously into a mosque during prayers.

Both pages: Extracts from *Land of Black Gold.*

There is comedy too when they make the mistake of picking up what appears to be a tube of aspirin and take a tablet each to ease their headaches. The tube contains "formula fourteen" used by the villain Müller and the foreign power backing him to spike petrol supplies. The detectives begin burping bubbles and start growing hair and beards at a phenomenal rate and in varying colours. The affliction is liable to return at any time despite powders developed by Calculus as an antidote. Their disconcerting discovery does at least thwart plans to disrupt international oil production.

They had already attained the height of comedy, for instance, when much earlier in *The Black Island*, handcuffed to each other, their pursuit of Tintin is abruptly "arrested" by an intervening lamppost.

THE ART OF GETTING NOTICED

These two plain-clothed detectives have a penchant for dressing-up. Their wish to blend in with the local population wherever they may be invariably causes them to stand out! In *Cigars of the Pharaoh,* disembarking at Port Said, they make their first foray in national, on this occasion Egyptian, dress. Trekking across the desert later, Tintin is startled to run across them again sitting by an oasis, this time in Bedouin garb. Giving chase, they trip up. "Clever dick! If I hadn't listened to you we wouldn't be wearing these nightshirts... and then we wouldn't have tripped ourselves up!" says Thomson.

Back in the desert in *Land of Black Gold,* they at first make no sartorial concessions to the heat. However, after they crash into a solitary palm tree believing it to be a mirage, they do take off their jackets – if not waistcoats – and tuck their handkerchiefs under their bowlers. Best of all, they don wonderfully old-fashioned one-piece red and white striped swimsuits for a dip into an oasis which does not exist – this time it is a mirage.

In *The Blue Lotus*, they make one of their great arrivals, reaching Hukow in full formal, traditional Chinese dress, pigtails and all. "Just as well we came in disguise..." mutters Thomson behind his fan. "Precisely!... Imagine the sensation we'd have caused, coming to a place like this in European clothes..."

Above: Frame from *The Blue Lotus*.

Right: Detail from *Land of Black Gold*.

Facing page: Detail from
Cigars of the Pharaoh.

Setting out aboard the Sirius in *Red Rackham's Treasure,* they change into matelot outfits to enable them to "mix discreetly with the ship's company." Thompson advises: "We must behave like old sea-dogs" and offers tobacco to chew – with singular results. Similarly Special Branch orders them to enlist as deckhands on the Speedol Star sailing for Khemikal, the chief port of Khemed, in *Land of Black Gold*. They rise to the occasion flamboyantly, finding their sailor suits and, apart from overnight bags and hat-boxes, they add life-vests, a life-ring and, amazingly, shrimping nets to their mari-

Below: Frame from
The Prisoners of the Sun.

time travelling gear. The name 'Titanic' is suitably embroidered on their navy berets. In the Moon adventure they make, not just in Snowy's view, a "sensational appearance" in Greek national costume and manacled having been detained as suspected parachutists who have violated the rocket research security zone. In *The Calculus Affair*, they appear in Swiss national dress, earrings included.

ACROBATICS AND TUMBLES GALORE

Hergé mastered the subtleties of staging the numerous acrobatics, spins and tumbles of the Thom(p)sons. The reader comes to anticipate them... if not the spectacular effects.

In *King Ottokar's Sceptre* the detectives intercept a parcel addressed to Tintin and opening it, detonate a shattering blast in the reporter's flat just as he returns. Spotting the potential assassins from the window, Tintin runs out in chase, the Thom(p)sons at his heels. He takes a motorcycle to con-tinue the pursuit and the detectives jump on behind him, but not for the first time in the adventures they fail to keep their hold on an accelerating vehicle and end up in a heap on the pavement as the reporter speeds off. It all started at the end of *Cigars of the Pharaoh* when Tintin borrows the Maharaja's racing car and they fail to hang on. It becomes a standard joke, along with their bowlers being blown off at every airport, and their unfail-ing propensity for getting soaked by falling into the sea. Additionally, their metal-heeled, hobnailed police boots guarantee that they go tumbling on polished surfaces.

Facing page
Top left: Frame from *The Crab with the Golden Claws*.
Top right: Frame from the original plate 94 of *The Crab with the Golden Claws*.
Below:
Frame from *King Ottokar's Sceptre*.

In *The Crab with the Golden Claws*, the Thom(p)sons are investigating a rash of counterfeit coins. Their enquiries lead them with Tintin onto the Karaboudjan, but they allow themselves to be duped by the First Mate, Allan Thompson, who plies them with whisky and Cuban cigars while Tintin is cracked on the head and tied up in the hold. They leave without him and, true to form, manage to fall down the ship's gangway.

Right: Detail from *King Ottokar's Sceptre*.

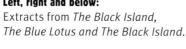

Left, right and below:
Extracts from *The Black Island*,
The Blue Lotus and *The Black Island*.

In *The Black Island* their pursuit of Tintin by aeroplane leads to them participating in an unintentionally astonishing sequence of aerobatics – a cup-winning display relayed live on television. In *The Calculus Affair* the detectives, in their ridiculous Swiss outfits, appear before the examining magistrate after being detained as suspicious characters. Having checked their credentials he directs them to the hospital where, after a spectacular fall on the highly polished floor, they themselves are admitted with multiple breakages just as Tintin and Haddock are discharged.

By the end of *The Crab with the Golden Claws* they are back in disguise, wearing hooded Arab gowns in the streets of the Moroccan port of Bagghar. Tintin spots them without much difficulty. Despite their pretence at being Arabs, they let themselves be kicked out of a mosque for forgetting to take off their shoes.

Above: Frame from *The Crab with the Golden Claws*.

Right: Extract from *The Black Island*.

If the constant tumbles of the detectives are a recurrent joke throughout *The Adventures*, their distinctive bowler hats offer Hergé further opportunities for humour. They may accidentally be jammed down to their ears, or made too small by Abdullah's trick of stuffing newspaper inside. They may be splattered with seagull droppings, blown away or flattened...

Above left: Frame from *The Calculus Affair*.
Above: Frame from *Red Rackham's Treasure*.
Below: Three frames from *The Secret of the Unicorn*.

Hergé would say he found bowler hats, together with telephones, particularly difficult to draw.

Left: Frame from the original plate 118 of *The Black Island*.

Below: Frame from *The Black Island*.

Above
Top: Frame from
The Castafiore Emerald.
Bottom: Frame from
The Calculus Affair.

Right:
Detail from
Cigars of the Pharaoh.

LINGUISTIC GYMNASTICS

The Thom(p)sons can cap their physical clumsiness, so reminiscent of the slapstick of the silent cinema, with linguistic contortion. Hergé would take as much care with the text as with drawing and his translators in different languages have tried hard to match the linguistic gymnastics of the original.

The Thom(p)sons are masters of sentence inflation and distortion, word jumbles and catchphrases such as

"To be precise!" or "Mum's the word!" The two detectives are linguistically disturbed. Thus in *The Castafiore Emerald* Tintin asks Haddock to call them to witness his theory about the theft of the emerald. For their part they remain adamant that the gipsies who had camped nearby are guilty. "It's as clear as day to us, eh Thompson?" To which the other agrees: "To be precise: dear as clay. That's my opinion and I'm stuck with it!"

Amid the myriad dyslexic possibilities of inverted letters or words, readers can delight in the range of examples scattered through *The Adventures,* such as the exchange in *Destination Moon*: "I don't know why, but it strikes me that Baxter and Wolff are behaving suspiciously," observes one detective, to which the other responds: "To be precise: most auspiciously."

Above: Frame from
The Castafiore Emerald.

Right: Detail from
Explorers on the Moon.

SELF-MOCKERY

While one is often amused at the expense of the two detectives, they too are capable of laughing at the absurd situations they sometimes find themselves in.

In *Explorers on the Moon* they find the time and the space suits to make a Moon walk: "Imagine! Here we are, strolling on the surface of the Moon, where the hand of man has never set foot!" Delighting in the reduced gravity and the apparent impossibility of taking a tumble, they even perform "a little ballet," which provokes great mutual mirth.

More often than not, however, their spasms of laughter presage another mishap. In *The Blue Lotus* they laugh at their last fall only to miss the stairs and come crashing down again. In *King Ottokar's Sceptre,* the hilarity over their fear of dropping into the sea precedes a fall... into the sea!

Facing page: Frames from
King Ottokar's Sceptre.

Left: Detail from *Explorers on the Moon.*

Below: Detail from *Tintin and Alph-Art.*

OMNIPRESENT

Their heroism before the firing squad in *Tintin and the Picaros* is not quite their final word, for they appear in Hergé's last unfinished adventure, *Tintin and Alph-Art,* which only exists in sketch form. There they arrive at Marlinspike and reveal they have information on a plot by "a Palestinian commando" to kidnap Emir Ben Kalish Ezab who is visiting the country, before themselves falling victim, together with Captain Haddock, to Abdullah's favourite type of terrorism – exploding cigars. Among recently rediscovered pages of sketches and notes for this ultimate adventure is one where Hergé has noted in red ink: "Cause the two Thom(p)sons to intervene: they are on a case involving drugs: a ship that... (So as to put the reader on a false trail.)" If this scenario were to be followed, then the two detectives would have ended their role in *The Adventures of Tintin* in much the same way as they had begun some 50 years earlier. They would have come full circle – in the manner of their desert drive – in a career of misunderstandings and mishaps. ■

THOMSON AND THOMPSON – "TO BE PRECISE!"